STEVE
SHARP

by
H. L. Dube

Steve Sharp

Steve was a cop. Now he works for himself.

Jaydeen

Jaydeen works for Steve.

Mrs Clayton

Mrs Clayton is rich.

ONE

Where can I find a missing kid?

Seventeen years old.

Clubs?

Pubs?

I start with clubs.

The Top Ten Club.

Bouncer on the door.

'You a member?' he says.

I show him the photo of the missing kid.

'Her name is Jo,' I say.

The bouncer acts stupid.

I slip him a twenty.

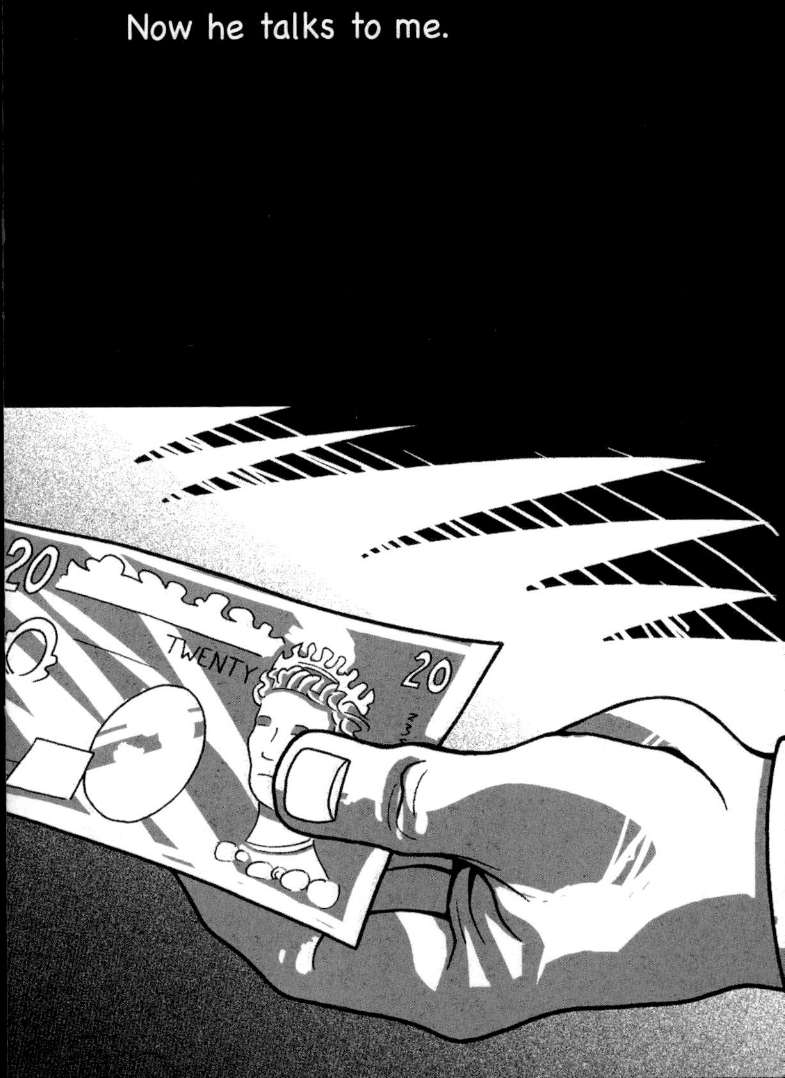
Now he talks to me.
20
TWENTY
20

'Is she in the club?' I ask.

The bouncer shakes his head.

'You see her, you ring me. OK?'

I give him the number.

TWO

I move round the town. All the clubs. All the pubs.

It costs me.

But no sign of Jo.

I walk on the main street.

My mobile rings.

Jo is in the Doodle Club.

With a guy.

I walk fast to the club.

'Jo is inside,' the guy says. 'With a drug dealer. Big John.'

'Look out for Big John,' he says.

I give him a twenty.

THREE

The place is full.

Flashing lights. Loud music.

I see Jo. She is dancing. With a big guy.

This is Big John.

Body like a bull. Arms like a gorilla. Face like a pig.

I walk over to Jo.

'Let's go, kid,' I say.

I touch her arm.

FOUR

There's a bang.

Like somebody put a bomb under the
club.

I see stars. I see lights.

But they are just in my head.

What happened?

Let me tell you.

Big John smacked me between my
eyes. A big bang.

I wake up.

My head feels like a train ran over me.

A guy gives me water. I drink it.

'Now get the hell out of my club,' he
says.

Two bouncers take my arms and march me out, like a frog.

Throw me in the street. Just like a frog.

Looks like they don't want me to speak to Jo.

Why is that?

STEVE SHARP

Now read
the next
Steve Sharp
book ....